MAKING THE GRADE GUITAR

GRADE 2

EASY POPULAR PIECES FOR YOUNG GUITARISTS. SELECTED AND ARRANGED BY DAVID BURDEN

Exclusive distributors:
Music Sales Limited
Newmarket Road, Bury St Edmunds, Suffolk IP33 3YB.
This book © Copyright 1999 Chester Music
ISBN 0-7119-7735-6
Order No.CH61612
Cover design and typesetting by Pemberton & Whitefoord
Printed in the United Kingdom by
Caligraving Limited, Thetford, Norfolk

Chester Music

(A division of Music Sales Limited)
8/9 Frith Street, London W1V 5TZ

INTRODUCTION

This collection of 17 popular tunes has been carefully arranged and graded to provide attractive teaching repertoire for young guitarists. The familiarity of the material will stimulate pupils' enthusiasm and encourage their practice, while introducing them to new techniques. Chords have been included where appropriate to give added flexibility to the arrangements. The technical demands increase through the book but the general standard is approximately Grade 2.

CONTENTS

WINTER
(FROM 'THE FOUR SEASONS')

By Antonio Vivaldi

Most of this piece is played in 2nd position. To get a contrast between the repeated
phrases (bars 9/10 & 11/12) use ponticello, as indicated, for the second one.
This is done by playing nearer the bridge than usual. *Norm.* indicates to return to the
normal place for striking the strings, towards the back of the sound hole.

YELLOW SUBMARINE

Words & Music by John Lennon & Paul McCartney

Most of this song is in 2nd position. * under a note indicates that,
instead of playing the note as written, tambora can be used if prefered.
This is done by tapping the bridge of the guitar with the side of the thumb
to produce the sort of drum sound used at that point in the recording by The Beatles.

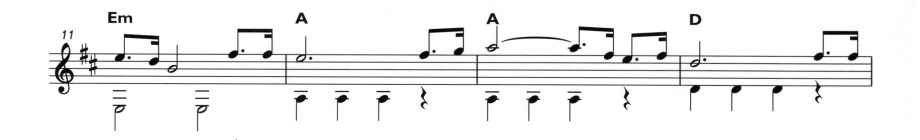

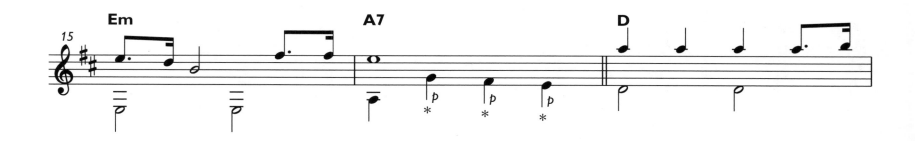

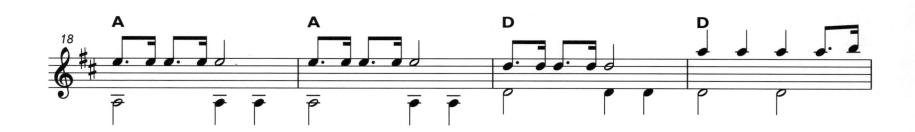

LOVE CHANGES EVERYTHING
FROM 'ASPECTS OF LOVE'

Music by Andrew Lloyd Webber
Lyrics by Don Black & Charles Hart

The bass line is important in maintaining the momentum in this song.
This bass part should be played very steadily, but do not let it drown out the melody.

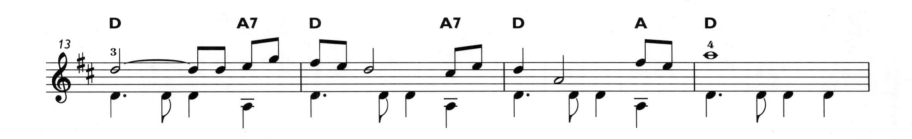

CLOSE EVERY DOOR

Music by Andrew Lloyd Webber
Lyrics by Tim Rice

This song should be played expressively throughout.
There is a crescendo into the major section in bar 16.
The final phrase has a decrescendo and rall. (slowing down).

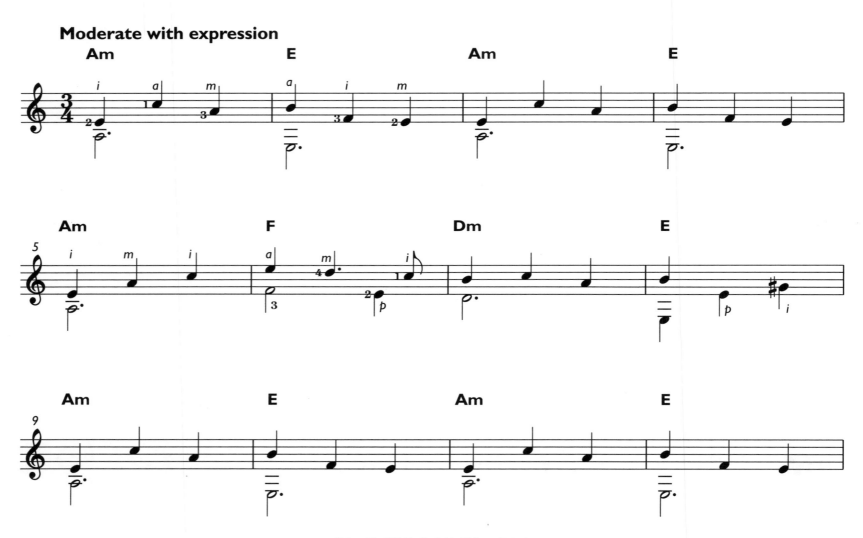

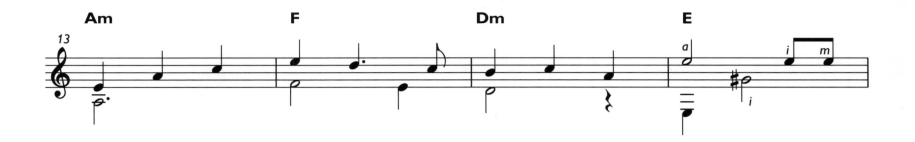

9

ANNIE'S SONG

Words & Music by John Denver

Try to let the melody sing out above the accompaniment, using rest stroke where possible, keeping it legato at all times, and making sure that all the notes are held on for their full values.

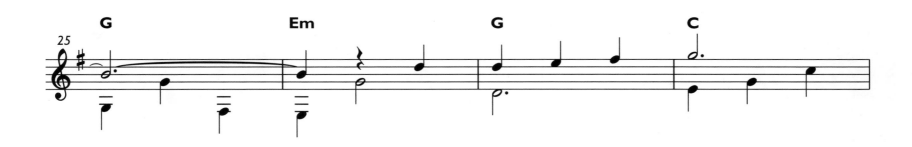

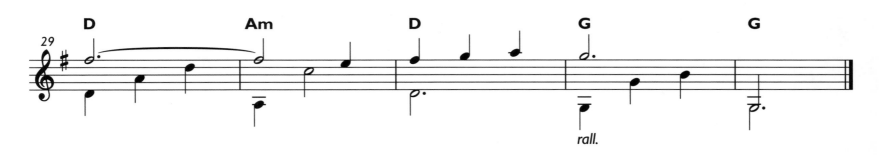

SPRING
(FROM 'THE FOUR SEASONS')

By Antonio Vivaldi

Most of this piece is in 2nd position.
To contrast the many repeated phrases, observe the tone and dynamic markings throughout.

Allegro

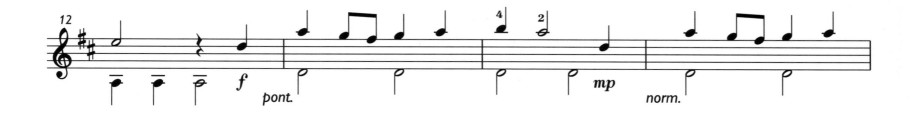

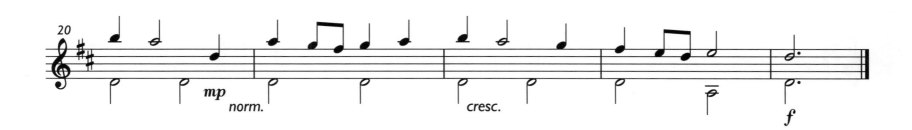

ALL MY LOVING

Words & Music by *John Lennon & Paul McCartney*

Try to hold the notes on for their full values in the melody and bass parts.

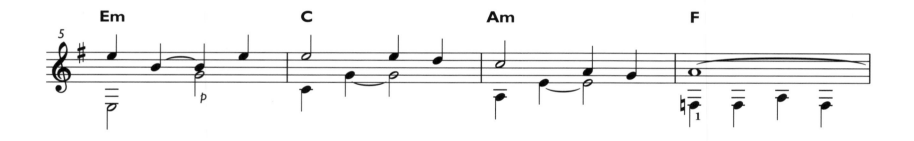

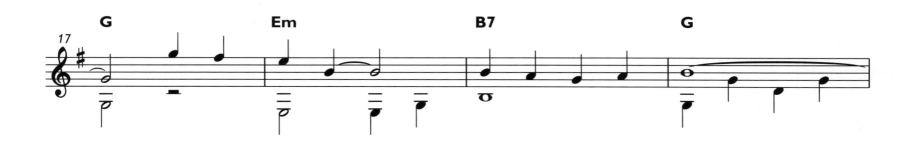

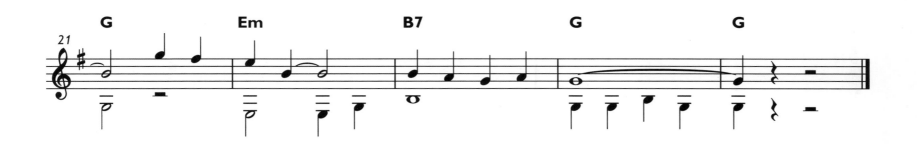

EASTENDERS

By Leslie Osborne & Simon May

Although this well known theme should not be played too fast, it should move along fluently.

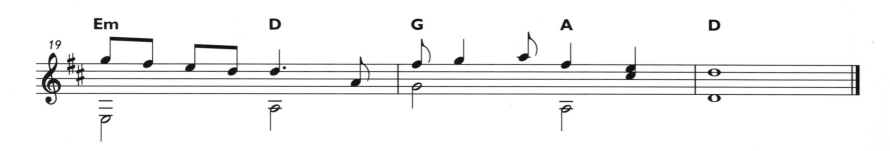

LAST OF THE SUMMER WINE

By Ronnie Hazlehurst

In this theme from the popular TV series keep a good balance between the melody
(the notes with the tails up) and the accompaniment (the notes with the tails down).

AMAZING GRACE

Words & Music by John Newton

Keep a good balance between the melody (the notes with the tails up) and the accompaniment
(the notes with the tails down) using rest stroke where possible.

With feeling

ANY DREAM WILL DO

Music by Andrew Lloyd Webber
Lyrics by Tim Rice

This song is in 3 sections. The outer 2 sections are virtually identical and should be played fluently.
Try to keep the dotted crotchet, quaver rhythm very crisp in the bass part (eg. bar 2).
This section should continue to build until bar 22.

MY FAVOURITE THINGS

Words by Richard Rodgers
Music by Oscar Hammerstein II

This song from 'The Sound of Music' should be played in a lively way.
In general emphasise the first beats of the bars and slightly stop the notes
on the 2nd and 3rd beats to produce something of a staccato sound.

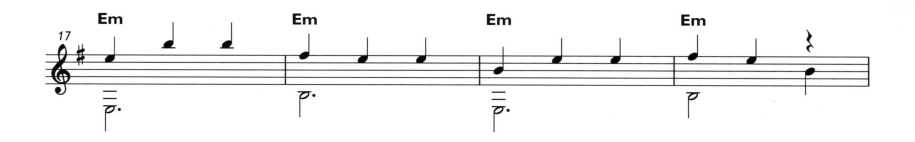

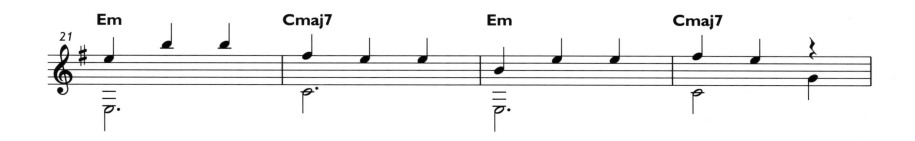

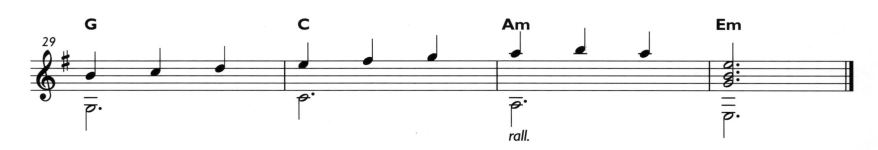

CHIM CHIM CHER-EE

Words & Music by Richard M. Sherman and Robert B. Sherman

This well known song from 'Mary Poppins' should be played lightly throughout.
There is a *rit.* (slowing down) at the end.